Lords of the Sky

Lords
of the
Sky

J. J. McCoy

Drawings by Kathleen Haven

THE **BOBBS-MERRILL** COMPANY, INC.
A SUBSIDIARY OF HOWARD W. SAMS & CO., INC.
Publishers • INDIANAPOLIS • NEW YORK

LIBRARY OF CONGRESS CATALOG NUMBER 63:11656

COPYRIGHT © 1963 BY J. J. MC COY
PRINTED IN THE UNITED STATES OF AMERICA
FIRST EDITION

For Hank Rosenkrantz, who watched the hawks with me in the Bald Eagle mountains of Pennsylvania.

Contents

Foreword

Thirty years ago, I saw my first bald eagle. It was a big moment for me and the other boys when we saw this great hawk. I can still recall the great excitement it caused.

We were standing on the stony beach of Treasure Island, the Boy Scouts' summer camp on the Delaware River, just below Frenchtown, New Jersey. It was early on a July morning. The camp was still asleep; only the cooks and "bird hikers" were out of bed.

A fine mist steamed up from the gurgling river. The sun wasn't up yet, but there was enough light to see across the river to the Pennsylvania shore. We clustered on the beach, peering around for any kind of bird. All we saw were some crows pushing and shoving each other on a nearby tree.

Suddenly, the Nature Counselor, George Davis, pointed to a large, dark bird winging up the river about two hundred yards offshore. Clutched in its talons was a big fish. Immediately, all binoculars and old-fashioned

9

field glasses were focused on the great bird. There were shouts of "Oh, boy!" and "Look at that!" Through our glasses we could make out the white head and tail.

"It's a bald eagle!" we all yelled, turning to George Davis for confirmation. He grinned and nodded. We were elated. A bald eagle! This was a bird we all knew about, but had seen only in photographs and at the zoo. Now here was one in all his wildness and splendor. The sight of that bald eagle more than repaid us for climbing out of our cots so early in the morning.

Ever since that morning on Treasure Island, I've been an ardent "hawk watcher." And I've been lucky enough to see more bald eagles, some golden eagles, and many lesser hawks.

As a soldier in World War II, I was stationed in various parts of the United States. Many of these posts were in excellent hawk country. The Okefenokee Swamp in Georgia, the Everglades in Florida, the Great Plains, and the Mexican Border—all provided me with many hours of fine hawking.

I still run for my binoculars when a hawk soars by. Unfortunately, some of the hawks are becoming scarce. Not many boys and girls have seen a peregrine falcon or a swallowtailed kite. Nor have they seen a bald or golden eagle outside of a zoo or museum of natural history. Yet, despite their decline, these hawks can still be seen in the wild.

LORDS OF THE SKY is an introduction to the American hawks, falcons, eagles, kites and vultures. It tells about the nature and habits of these unusual birds, the ancient art of the falconer, and the senseless slaughter of the hawks.

It is hoped that this little book will win new friends for the hawks. They are valuable birds that need more understanding and protection. I also hope that all who read this book will decide to aim binoculars, instead of shotguns, at the hawks.

Lords of the Sky

1

The Nature of Hawks

With vibrant wings tipping this way and that soar the hawks. Then, with folded wings, they plummet down on their prey in a wind-whistling dive. And perched on a dead branch, they scream their defiance across the wilderness. They are proud and fearless lords of the sky, ruling their aerial domain with speed and power.

The hawks, eagles, kites, falcons and vultures are all related. They belong to the order *Falconiformes*, or daytime birds of prey. Most of them are hunters, a few are scavengers. The hunter-hawks, those that catch live prey, feed on birds, mammals, reptiles, amphibians, and insects. One of them, the everglade kite, is a food specialist. This hawk feeds exclusively on the water moon snail. The scavenger-hawks, such as the turkey vulture, California condor and caracara, feed on carrion. Both the hunters and scavengers play an important role in nature.

Since the hawklike birds are related, we'll refer to them collectively as hawks. When discussing a particular group of hawks, we'll give them the group name, such as falcons, Accipiters, eagles, etc. And when mentioning a specific hawk, we'll use the common name.

The most striking features of the hawks are their powerful beaks and talons. The beak is short, curving

sharply into a hooked tip. There is a sharp cutting edge
to the beak, enabling the hawk to tear or rip its prey.
Falcons have a notch and one or two "teeth" on the
upper part of their beaks.

All of the hawks, except the vultures, have short legs
with razor-sharp talons. The old-time falconer called
the talons "pounces." In catching their prey, the hawks
stretch out their legs, open their talons and then quickly
snatch or bind onto the victim. Each foot has four talons,
three in front and one in back. While the hawks alight
on the ground, they move with difficulty. Only the
vultures are at home on the ground. As carrion eaters,
they must come down to earth, so nature has equipped
them with feet and claws adapted for ground work. The
legs and claws of the vultures are similar to those of a
turkey.

Hawks have keen eyes. They are far-sighted and no
movement escapes them. Watch a turkey vulture
through binoculars. You will see him move his head
from side to side, scanning the landscape below. Or
watch a kestrel darting over a field, searching for grasshoppers. Just let a grasshopper stretch a leg and the
kestrel is on to him with a lightninglike plunge!

The hawk's eyes are round and have a piercing gaze.
It is a gaze of defiance and courage. All of the falcons
have dark brown or black eyes. The other hawks have
yellow or orange eyes.

Hawks are well-feathered birds. Their plumage is
geared for the stress and strain of swift flight. The wings
and tail are short, broad or long, depending upon the

*Strong-beaked and keen-eyed, the hawks are
mighty hunters*

species. Like other birds, the hawks shed or molt their feathers. But they have a gradual molt, sometimes taking as long as six months for a complete change of feathers. Other birds molt in a much shorter time.

Wise old Mother Nature has a good reason for giving the hawks a longer molting period. As aerial hunters, they must fly to eat. Other birds in molt can find food on trees, bushes or on the ground and in water. But not the hawks. So Mother Nature keeps them flying while they shed a few feathers at a time.

Hawks capture their prey by speed and stealth. The swift falcons hunt in open country. They rely entirely upon their superior speed to catch birds and insects. Falcons mount high above their victim, fold their wings and dive down with incredible speed. The peregrine falcon, for instance, has been clocked at speeds over 160 miles per hour while in a dive or "stoop." Falcons either fasten onto the prey or knock it out of the sky.

Broad-winged and short-winged hawks hunt in and around wooded areas. They are not as fast as the falcons. But they are very quick and agile, twisting and darting with astonishing mobility. The woodland hawks are often seen perched on a tree or circling above a woods or hedgerow. When they spot a mouse or bird, they dart down and fasten onto the prey.

All in all, Nature has divided up the hunting range according to the talents of the hawks. Woods, fields, prairies, deserts, marshes and rivers—all have a hawk assigned to hunt over the area. Even the cities are covered. It is not unusual to find a peregrine or kestrel hunting in the concrete and steel canyons of our big cities.

Most of the hawks build their nests or aeries in trees, atop cliffs, in caves, and sometimes on the ledges of sky-scrapers. One hawk, the harrier or marsh hawk, builds his nest close to the ground in or near swamps. Vultures are not too particular and build their nests in hollow logs or abandoned buildings. And the big fish hawk, the osprey, doesn't hesitate to place his large aerie on the crossbars of a telephone or electric line pole.

Both the male and female hawks make good parents, taking turns in incubating the eggs and feeding the young. There are a few exceptions to this—the golden eagle and the osprey, for instance. While male golden eagles and osprey hunt and bring food to the female, they do not help incubate the eggs.

Hawks usually have small families. Breeding begins in late March or early April, and the females lay from one to five eggs, depending upon the species. Both the male and female are kept busy hunting and carrying food back to the hungry babies. Females are larger than males by approximately one-third. Since he is a third smaller, the male is called a tercel. The word comes from the Latin, *tertius*, meaning the third. Despite his smaller size, the tercel is a fierce and tireless hunter.

Newborn hawks are very weak and, while hungry, cannot rip or tear their food. At birth, the beaks are soft and pliable. Therefore, the mother hawk must prepare the food for the babies. She does this by tearing off bits of food and holding them in her beak. Each baby hawk

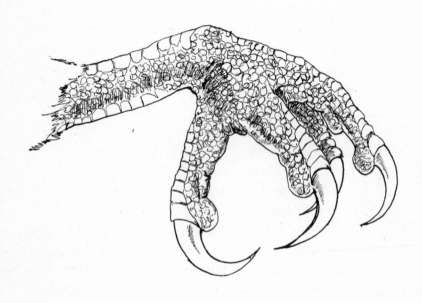

Razor-sharp talons or "pounces" grip the hawk's prey

then pecks these bits of food from the mother's beak. Later, when the youngsters are stronger, they quickly snatch the prey from the mother and devour it. Very often the young hawks will fight over the prey, and the strongest one eats first.

The young hawks are brought up in a hard school. Weaklings do not survive. Young hawks must learn to fly and to catch prey. Some baby hawks are killed while learning to fly. They either fall or jump off a cliff or high tree before they are ready. This often happens when the youngsters are fighting over food.

When the young hawks have their flight feathers, the parents urge them to try their wings. The protesting eyases are pushed out of the aerie and off the cliff or tree. Some of them quickly learn to flap their wings and fly around awkwardly. Others drop and then nervously stretch out their wings, gliding down to a lower tree or ledge. Here they perch and complain in a loud voice. But, one by one, the nestlings learn to fly.

Baby hawks begin their hunting lessons by flying out to meet a parent bringing home its prey. The parent-hawk flies around the aerie, enticing a youngster up to her. Then she drops the prey and the young hawk must catch it. After the young hawk has become adept at catching prey from his mother, he learns to hunt and catch his own.

When the young hawks have learned to hunt, the older hawks drive them away from the aerie. They also chase the youngsters out of the immediate area. This may seem like harsh treatment on the part of the parents.

But there is a good reason for it. Hunting among the hawks is very competitive. Too many hawks in the same area would soon drive away any game. While birds and mammals living in a vicinity might risk a few hawks, they would move away when the hawk population became too large. And so the young hawks must leave home and find a new place to live and hunt.

Nearly all of the hawks that breed in the northern United States and Canada migrate south in winter. The hawks migrate mostly because of the food problem. Small birds fly south and small mammals hole up for the winter. Insects and amphibians disappear in the north when the frost comes. The hawks, themselves, can stand cold weather. But they must eat and so to the south they go where they find plenty of food.

The hawk migrations begin in early September, when the weather is still fair and the breezes blow. As the time for migrating nears, the hawks become restless. Some of them, such as the broad-winged hawks, gather in flocks, circling and soaring in preparation for the flight southward. Then, when a windy day comes along, they mount to the sky and ride the breezes down the flyways.

It is a thrilling sight to see hundreds of hawks, maybe thousands, soaring down the North American flyways. The main flyways are the Appalachian mountains in the east, the Mississippi valley and the Rocky mountains in the west. One of the most popular flyways (at least as far as hawk watchers are concerned) is one that passes over the Kittatinny mountain range in eastern Pennsylvania. Here, on top of Hawk Mountain, near Hamburg,

Pennsylvania, the hawk watchers are treated to a spectacular display of hawks, eagles, falcons and vultures soaring along on the wind.

Unfortunately, some of the flyways have become death-traps for migrating hawks. Ignorant and lawless hunters have killed thousands of hawks from shooting blinds atop the ridges. This wanton destruction of hawks is a shameful waste of our natural resources. Regretfully, it still goes on.

Hawks are majestic birds. True, they kill other birds and small mammals. But that is their nature. However, hawks kill quickly and without torture. They do not play with their victims, as does the cat with a mouse. They strike suddenly and, nine times out of ten, the victim is killed outright.

Nature has made all creatures dependent upon each other for survival. Every bird, mammal (including man), reptile, fish and insect preys upon some other form of life. It is the law of nature, the law of survival of the fittest.

Hawks play a major role in the balance of nature. They help to regulate the bird and mammal populations. Nature provides checks and balances to keep populations under control. Hawks are one of these checks and balances. For example, the Buteos or broad-winged hawks prey on rodents and other harmful mammals. And the Mississippi kite kills grasshoppers, locusts and other harmful insects.

When the hawks are killed or driven away, the balance of nature is upset. There are many examples of this upset

The outer parts of a hawk

balance, among animal predators, as well as hawks. Coyotes, for instance, hunt rabbits. In those areas where bounties on coyotes result in a reduction of the coyote population, rabbits increase. Likewise for the golden eagle and gophers. Golden eagles prey on gophers, rodents that can do great damage to wheat. Unfortunately for him, the golden eagle also likes to eat poultry and young animals. He then becomes an outlaw and is killed. But when the golden eagles are killed and driven away, the gopher population increases. And so it goes. The hawks are both beneficial and harmful, but the good they do far outweighs the bad.

Hawks also eliminate sick birds and mammals. And the work of the scavenger-hawks, the vultures, certainly needs no defense. If it were not for these carrion-eaters, water pollution and disease would increase.

Man has never domesticated the proud hawks. He has captured them and dominated those in captivity. But he has not been able to change their basic nature. Hawks are still wild birds. Like the elephants, hawks rarely, if ever, breed in captivity. And a "tame" hawk turned loose will speedily revert to a wild state.

Ice Age man made friends with the wild dogs. His successors, the Stone Age men, domesticated animals and had them work for the good of the tribes. Hunters had dogs to scent and chase game and fast horses on which to keep up with the dogs. But this was not enough; man wanted an aerial hunter. Wingless himself, man turned his attention to the hawks. Soon he found that with patience and training he could get the hawks to hunt for him. Thus, the art of falconry was born.

2

Falconry

A medieval horseman canters across the field, a hooded peregrine falcon perched on his gloved fist. High overhead, a flock of ducks wings through the sky. The falconer reins in his horse, slips off the falcon's plumed hood and boosts the bird into the air with a toss of his wrist. Up streaks the falcon, climbing with fast wing beats.

Now she has mounted high above the hurrying ducks. From the falconer below comes the cry, "Hey, gar, gar!" It is the signal urging the falcon on to the quarry.

Folding her wings, the falcon plummets down in a vertical dive or stoop. Talons outstretched, she plunges onto a duck on the outside of the flock.

"Who-whoop!" shouts the falconer as the falcon strikes the duck.

There is a puff of feathers and the duck tumbles earthward. Down drops the falcon, warily following the falling duck. Both duck and falcon hit the ground almost at the same time, and the falcon pounces on the duck with her talons.

The falconer quickly rides up and dismounts. Striding over to the falcon and quarry, he bends down on one knee, holding his gloved fist out to the quivering falcon. She eyes him fiercely. Then the falconer gives a low whistle. Still bristling with the excitement of the hunt, the falcon reluctantly leaves the dead duck and hops up on the falconer's glove. Next, the falconer neatly slips the leather hood over the falcon's head and eyes. He strokes her with a feather and she quiets down. Then, picking up the duck, the falconer mounts his horse and the hunters dash off.

This was the ancient sport of falconry!

Falconry is an old sport, nearly as old as hunting with dogs. It began in the Orient, among the hunters and nomadic tribesmen of China and eastern Asia. Chinese falconers were flying eagles and falcons as early as 2,000 B.C. Kublai Khan, the founder of the Mongolian dynasty in China, kept a hunting force of more than five hundred falcons.

As trade increased between east and west, the art of the falconer moved westward. Soon the Hindus, Persians, Arabians and Egyptians adopted falconry as a means of adding to their food supply. In the time of the pharaohs, hawks and falcons were kept as hunting birds and objects of worship. Horus, the Egyptian god of day, had the body of a man and the head of a hawk. The sacred Egyptian hawk frequently appears in the ancient hieroglyphics.

Just when falconry came to Europe is not known. But falconers in France, Holland, Germany and Poland sent their falcons aloft more than a thousand years ago. The Anglo-Saxons and their hawks hunted the British

The Arabs prized their hunting falcons

moors as far back as A.D. 860. Alfred the Great, King of the West Saxons, was an ardent falconer.

King Canute, monarch of England and Denmark, kept a large number of falcons. There is a legend that tells how King Canute sat on the beach and commanded the waves to come to him. Needless to say, the waves didn't obey Canute and came up only as far as the tide permitted. When he wasn't commanding the sea to come to him, Canute was out on the moors flying his falcons.

William the Conqueror, Duke of Normandy, brought falcons and falconers with him when he invaded England in 1066. William also brought over a name for this exciting sport. The term "falconry" comes from an old Norman word, *fauconnerie*. It means the art of training hawks and falcons to hunt on command. Harold, the British king defeated by William in the Battle of Hastings, was also a falconer of high regard.

But the most accomplished falconer of all times was Frederick II, Holy Roman Emperor and King of Sicily. On his vast estates in Sicily, Frederick maintained a large establishment of the finest hunting hawks and falcons in the world. This great falconer not only trained and hunted with hawks, but studied their nature and habits. Much of what Frederick observed about hawks back in the thirteenth century has been proven scientifically sound. He was a true falconer, a man who loved these proud birds.

Falconry reached its peak in England in the Middle Ages. The early Englishmen were a people fond of hunting. King, nobleman and clergyman all went a-hawking. At first, the sport was reserved for royalty and nobility; later, clergyman and yeoman were accepted into the falconer's circle. Each class had a special hunting hawk. There were eagles and gyrfalcons for kings, peregrines for noblemen, merlins for ladies, kestrels for clergymen and goshawks for yeomen. The yeomen were commoners who attended the nobility. They were the only commoners permitted to hunt with hawks and falcons.

The medieval English falconer placed a high value on his hunting hawks and they were considered private property. Stealing a hawk or falcon was a serious crime. Edward III issued an edict in 1362 making the theft of a hawk a crime punishable by death. Edward's edict stated: "If any man steal a hawke and the same carry away, it shall be done of him as of a thief of a horse." Horse thieves in medieval England were strung up on the gallows.

While most of the nobility hunted with hawks purely for the sport, there were other falconers who hunted to put food on the table. Many hunters soon found that hawks and falcons were more effective against high-flying birds than the longbow or crossbow. There were a few expert archers who could hit a bird with an arrow or crossbolt; but the average hunter wasn't so lucky. If he wanted to eat snipe or woodcock, he had to hunt with a hawk or falcon.

Eventually, the laws governing the keeping and training of hawks were eased in England. More people became falconers and went hawking. Most falconers flew

The Africans learned the art of the falconer from their Oriental neighbors

their hawks against pheasant, duck, woodcock and snipe. Some falconers, who were not so particular, sent their hawks up against crows, rooks, gulls, jays, magpies and blackbirds.

Various hawks and falcons were used to hunt British game birds. Among them were the gyrfalcon, peregrine, kestrel, merlin, hobby and goshawk. The largest was the big gyrfalcon from Greenland. The "gyr" part of his name comes from the Greek *gyri*, meaning lord. British falconers also used the saker and loriner, European falcons, and the Barbary falcon.

Over in the Netherlands, Dutch and Flemish falconers sent their falcons after heron. It might be supposed that the ungainly heron was a poor match for a speedy falcon. But such was not the case. The heron was often able to dodge out of the way of a stooping falcon. And many a falcon had to work hard to catch a heron.

The Dutch were expert falconers and contributed much to the sport. Some of the falcon's equipment or "furniture" was designed by early Dutch falconers. For example, the Dutch hood, a stiff leather hat tied by two thongs, was a Dutch contribution. So were the jesses, the small leather straps that go around the falcon's feet.

Falconry in America never reached the heights of popularity as in England and the Netherlands. This is easily understood. By the time America was discovered, gunpowder had been invented. Colonial American hunters were armed with blunderbusses and fowling pieces. But there were some American falconers who sent their hawks up after birds and small mammals. The most popular of the early American hunting hawks were the American peregrine falcon, prairie falcon, merlin, kestrel, Cooper's hawk and the goshawk.

Even though falconry has declined in favor of hunting with guns, it is not a dead or forgotten sport. Hunting hawks still mount to the sky in China, England, India, Iran, France, Japan, Russia, Germany, Poland and the North African countries. Rare sport though it may be, falconry is still put to use. In some countries, hawks and falcons are used to chase flocks of birds away from airfields. Very often these flocks of birds endanger planes landing and taking off. But with hawks and falcons on hand and ready to attack, the small birds soon find another place to congregate.

In parts of Mongolia and Lapland, falconers hunt deer and wolves with huge eagles. A few years ago, a foreign film called "The Valley Of The Eagles" was shown in America. Although the film dealt with the Nazi occupation of the Scandinavian countries, it had some exciting scenes on hunting with eagles.

The falconers in the film were Laplanders who lived at the base of a large mountain. They lived in constant dread of an avalanche. Consequently, they used no guns in hunting, for fear of the shots' setting off a snow- or landslide. They used eagles as a substitute for guns.

A group of men, escaping from the Nazis by dog sled, came into the region of the Lapland falconers. They were pursued by large wolves. Near the big mountain, the group stopped their flight and tried to beat off the wolves with clubs and rifle butts. Their ammunition had long

Both lord and lady went a-hawking in medieval England

since given out. The wolves fought back, killing some sled dogs and slashing the men. When the wolves withdrew a short distance, the exhausted men braced themselves for another attack.

Suddenly, into the valley galloped a troop of Laplanders mounted on reindeer. Each of them had a large eagle perched on a wooden pole with a crossbar. The ends of the poles were stuck into the stirrups like cavalry guidons. One by one, the Laplanders released their eagles into the air. With powerful wing beats and talons outstretched, the eagles flew at the wolves. Striking with terrific force, the eagles sunk their talons into the necks and backs of the wolves, forcing them to the ground. There they held the struggling wolves until the Laplanders rode up and killed the wolves with clubs and spears. Their work finished, the eagles hopped back on their perches and leisurely preened their feathers!

As long as there are hawks and men who admire them, falconry will still live. And wherever falconers gather, they discuss and argue over the relative merits of the different hawks and falcons. Some of their arguments are as heated as any about baseball or politics. And sometimes, only the patron saint of the falconer, Saint Bavo of Valkenswaard, can settle them!

3

The Falconer's Art

Frederick II pointed out that a falconer must be kind, gentle, and patient. These qualifications are just as necessary today as they were in Frederick's time. Hawks and falcons are wild birds, easily excited and quick to anger. A short temper or rough handling on the part of the falconer results in an irritated bird and frustrated handler. From the time he obtains a hawk or falcon, the falconer must exercise patience.

Hawks and falcons don't need to be taught *how* to hunt. They are natural hunters. But they must be taught to hunt at the falconer's command. And the medieval falconer taught his hawk or falcon to do just that with remarkable skill. While the falconer could teach his bird to attack a bird or mammal, he could not get the hawk or falcon to retrieve. He had to do his own retrieving of game.

Before we learn more about the falconer's art, it will be helpful to know some of his vocabulary. It is rich with colorful words and phrases. There are more than six hundred words and terms used by the falconer. Several of them have found their way into modern usage. Here are the words and terms used in this chapter:

Aerie or *eyrie*: the nest of the hawk, falcon or eagle.

Bate: to spring off the perch or fist in an attempt to fly away. Hawks and falcons often bate when frightened.

Bell: a small bell that is fastened to the hawk's feet, one to each foot. Bells of different pitch are used and help the falconer keep track of his hawk or falcon.

Bewit: a small leather strap used to hold the bell on the bird's foot.

Bind: to fasten onto the prey with the talons or pounces.

Castings: bits of bones, feathers and skin. Captive hawks not fed on birds or mammals need castings several times a week.

Come to: to obey the falconer's command to come to the fist. This is similar to teaching a dog to come.

Creance: a long line used to swing the lure.

Eyas: a young hawk or falcon taken from the aerie.

Falcon: in falconry, the female hawk or falcon.

Fully-summed: a hawk or falcon that is in full plumage.

Furniture: the equipment of a hawk or falcon. It includes the bell, bewit, hood, jesse and leash.

Hack: young hawks and falcons allowed to fly at liberty are said to be flying "at hack."

Hack board: a special board or perch used to feed the young hawks and falcons flying at hack.

Hood: a head and eye covering made from leather. It is placed over the bird's eyes to quiet her. The three

*A boost from the falconer's wrist
and the falcon is up and away!*

major types of hoods are the rufter (a training hood), Dutch and Indian.

Imp: to fix or repair a feather. It is a splicing tchnique.

Jesse: a short leather strap that goes around the hawk's feet.

Leash: a leather strap, usually flat, that is fastened to the swivel, which is hooked onto the jesses.

Lure: a training dummy or device used to bring the hawk or falcon back to the fist. It is usually made of leather and designed to more or less resemble a bird. Bird wings are fastened to the sides of the lure. The lure is swung around in the air by the falconer, who holds the lure on the end of a long line or creance.

Man: to handle or gentle a hawk or falcon.

Mews: place where hawks and falcons were kept when in molt. In modern usage, the word means a row of stables or garages.

Passage hawk: a young hawk or falcon taken during migration.

Quarry: the prey or victim of a hawk or falcon.

Stoop: the swift descent of a falcon onto her prey.

Waiting on: the circling of a hawk or falcon above the head of the falconer.

Weathering: exposing a hawk or falcon to strange people, dogs, sounds, sights, etc.

Weathering block: a log or block of wood placed upright in the ground and used as a perch.

In the heydey of falconry, hawks and falcons were secured in several ways. Falconers climbed cliffs and trees and took eyases from the aeries, or they caught passage hawks. Some falconers bought hawks and falcons in the special markets in Europe and Asia. Passage hawks were caught either in nets or in "pole traps." The pole traps were steel spring traps fastened to the end of a long pole. They were padded to prevent injury to the hawk's feet. These pole traps were baited with a live bird and when a migrating hawk pounced on the bait, he sprung the trap and was caught.

When the falconer of old took an eyas from the aerie, he made no attempt to train it right away. First of all, the eyas was still a nestling and had to learn to fly. Young hawks and falcons were usually kept in an old shed or barn. Here, the falconer provided them with a nest made from an old hamper or deep basket. He fastened a flat perch or hack board to the rim of the basket. The eyases were fed three times a day on the hack board, and that was all the attention they received. But the feeding on the hack board was very important. It was the only control the falconer had over the young hawks.

In four or five weeks, the young hawks were flying at hack. The falconer hoped the young hawks would return to the barn or shed when they got hungry. And most of them did come back. But now and then, an eyas would fly away; however, this was a risk the falconer had to take. Regardless of the risk, the falconer had to let the eyases fly at hack. It was an important step in developing their wings and fitting them for the job of hunter.

The falconer usually tried to discourage the young hawks from catching prey while flying at hack. Once

Top: *Leather hoods calmed easily excited falcons by preventing them from seeing*

Bottom: *Small bells helped the falconer to locate his birds*

they killed and ate the prey, the eyases would stay away from the hack board. So the falconer tied large bells onto the legs of the eyases. These bells made a loud noise that usually scared off any prey. Sometimes, even the big bells failed to stop an eyas from catching a bird. When an eyas failed to return to the hack board, the falconer knew she had killed. If and when she came back, the falconer started immediately to train her.

If the falconer captured a passage hawk, he omitted the hack board feeding and flying at hack. He would start with the manning and training of the hawk. Most falconers, however, preferred to work with eyases. They were easier to obtain and learned their lessons more quickly than a passage hawk.

The falconer's first step in training the eyas or passage hawk was to accustom the bird to his voice, movements, and gloved fist. So, for the first day or two, falcon and falconer became acquainted.

Before the falcon was manned, she was fitted with special equipment or furniture. Jesses were fastened around her legs just above the talons. The end of the jesses were then hooked to the swivel, which, in turn, was fastened to the falconer's leash. Above the jesses, the falconer tied the bells with bewits. Finally, the eyas was fitted with a rufter hood of soft leather which was open at the back.

The falconer equipped himself with a heavy leather glove or gauntlet. This was either a left or right hand glove, depending upon the falconer's nationality. American, English and European falconers carried their falcons on the left hand. Asiatic and North African falconers kept their birds on the right hand.

All of the preliminary manning was done in a darkened room. Most birds quiet down in the dark and can be approached and handled. Every farm boy knows that the easiest way to catch a flighty white leghorn chicken is to wait until dark. Then the chicken can be lifted off its roost without a squawk coming from the bird. And so it was with the falconer—he handled and fitted the furniture on his falcon in a darkened room. When he took the bird outside, he put the rufter hood over the falcon's head and eyes.

The falconer taught the eyas to feed from his hand by taking a piece of meat and dragging it over the bird's feet. This attracted the bird's attention and she would usually snap at the meat. When she snapped, the falconer dropped a piece of meat into her mouth. As she swallowed the meat, the falconer gave a low whistle. This feeding and whistling routine was followed at every meal. Soon, the falcon learned to associate the whistle with food.

Next, the falconer taught the eyas to jump up and perch on his gloved fist. He did this by using food to lure the bird to his fist. After the falcon learned to jump up on the fist, she was carried about by the falconer. Now and then, the falconer spoke to the bird and stroked her with a feather. He was careful not to startle the falcon and make her bate. Since she was fastened by the jesses and leash, bating would injure her plumage. When a falcon bated, she hung upside down, flapping or beat-

Top: *A hooded falcon perched on a gloved fist*

Bottom: *Falcon "furniture"—jesses, leash, swivel, bells and leather gauntlet*

ing her wings as she tried to right herself. This beating of the wings often resulted in broken flight feathers. Then the falconer had to imp or repair the feathers.

After the falcon had learned to feed from the falconer's hand, jump up to the fist and be carried about, the rufter hood was exchanged for either a Dutch or Indian hood. The Dutch hood was made from three pieces of leather and tied with two leather thongs. It had a tighter fit than the rufter hood. The Indian hood was made from a single piece of leather and tied around the bottom. It had one main disadvantage: the falcon could claw or scratch it off.

When the falconer had thoroughly manned the falcon, he turned next to the task of weathering her. While she was accustomed to the presence, voice, and touch of the falconer, she had to be introduced to other people, dogs, cats and various sounds of the area outside the shed or barn.

The weathering blocks or perches were set up on a lawn or other suitable place. Falcons were put on thick blocks or logs fixed into the ground and rising three or four feet. The falcon was tied to the block by a line attached to her jesses. Since falcons prefer to rest on flat surfaces, the block or log was satisfactory.

Short-winged hawks prefer to perch on branches, so the falconer put them on branch-like perches or special "bow" perches. The bow perch was usually a large, oval iron ring with an iron stake at the lower end. The perch was forged out of one piece of iron, with the stake in the center of the lower arc of the perch. Both the block and bow perches were equipped with small rings for fastening the leash or line.

Since hawks and falcons often bated while being weathered, the falconer took some precautions. He laced leather thongs across the open space of the bow perch, similar to a loose stringing of a tennis racquet. A hawk that bated on one of these laced perches didn't hang down in the ring, but braced against the lacing and righted herself. Another protective device was the "screen," a loop of canvas hung down in back of a perch. When a hawk bated, she flapped against the canvas and pushed herself upright.

Before a hawk or falcon was flown against any quarry, she was introduced to the lure. The falconer used the lure to bring the bird back to his fist; consequently, the lure had a piece of meat securely fastened to it. The falcon soon learned to associate the lure with food.

The lure was usually a small stuffed leather sack, trimmed with pigeon wings or feathers. It was weighted, so that it could be whirled around on the end of a ten-foot line or creance. However, the falconer was careful not to hit the falcon with the weighted lure. If he did accidentally hit the falcon, he would have a difficult time in getting the bird to come near the lure.

In training the falcon to come to the lure, the falconer used an assistant. Standing ten or fifteen feet away, the falconer gave a signal and the assistant unhooded the falcon. Then the falconer whirled the lure around his head and the falcon was tossed into the air by the

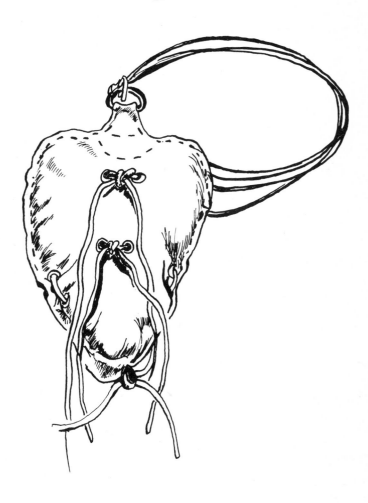

The falconer's lure was used to bring the bird back to the fist

assistant. As the falcon came to the lure, the falconer let it drop to the ground. The falcon usually dove on it. When she did, the falconer got down on one knee and held out his gloved fist.

Some hawks, such as the goshawk, often ignored the lure. When this happened, the falconer had to try some tricks. He would drag the lure along the ground, making it hop and roll. If he made the lure seem lifelike—like a mouse or rat—the goshawk pounced on it.

Gradually, the distance between the falconer and the falcon was increased, so that the bird was coming to the lure from as far away as 200 yards. Next, the falconer taught the falcon how to turn and stoop on the lure. He whirled the lure around his head, the falcon circling or waiting on above his head. Then, just as the falcon dove at the lure, he yanked it away. This forced the falcon to check its stoop, whirl around, find the lure and dive on it again. This was an important lesson for the eyas; not every hawk or falcon catches its prey on the first stoop.

The old-time falconer paid strict attention to the feeding of his birds. A poorly-fed falcon or hawk was worthless as a hunter. Overfeeding or gorging made a bird lazy and took all of the hunting spirit out of her. She was like a fat cat; since her stomach was full, there was no need to hunt.

Hawks have odd stomachs. Part of the hawk's stomach, the pannel, is lined with thick mucous. This mucous has to be cleared out at regular intervals. Nature does this by having the hawk eat bones, skin, fur and feathers. These are swirled around in the hawk's stomach until they become impacted into pellets or castings. These castings swab out the mucous and are coughed up by the hawk.

Captive hawks, however, were not always fed on birds or small mammals, but sometimes on fresh beef. Hawks that did not get whole birds or mammals had to be given castings two or three times a week to prevent digestive troubles.

The falconer fed his birds with an eye to maintaining the average weight of their species. This meant that he would have to weigh the hawks now and then. He never fed them cold or tainted meat, since to do so would be to invite digestive upsets. And he kept his birds in good flying condition, feeding them once a day and fasting them for one day before sending them after prey.

Falconers today follow much the same methods in training their hawks and falcons. Some falconers have their own special tricks of the trade. Others use the classical methods of Frederick II and other noted falconers.

Today, the taking and keeping of a hawk or falcon is prohibited in most of the United States. State laws are strict about this, and the federal government protects the bald and golden eagles. A few states, such as New York, permit hawks and falcons to be kept and trained upon the issuance of a special license. But not everyone can get one of these licenses; the applicant must know what he's about and show more than mere curiosity about hawks.

But while falconry is a rare sport in America, hawk watching is a very popular one. Anyone can participate in hawk watching and the rewards are many. Peregrines, gyrfalcons and goshawks can still be seen stooping at their prey, while far below them, the ghosts of the old-time falconers urge them on to the quarry with wind-borne shouts of "Hey, gar, gar!"

4

Falcons

Nimble aerialists and superb hunters, the falcons are the fastest of all the hawks. They have long, pointed wings and fly with rapid wing beats—mounting high above their prey, then descending in a high-powered dive or stoop.

The largest of the falcons is the gyrfalcon (*Falco rusticolis*), a skilled hunter of the Arctic coastal plains. He has the most northern range of all the daytime birds of prey and is found in Greenland, Siberia and Alaska, southward into the northern United States, the British Isles and central Europe.

In severe winters, the gyrfalcon may visit as far south as New England, New York and Pennsylvania. They have been sighted near New York City, flying along the ocean front. Gyrfalcons are also seen now and then over the Kittatinny mountain range in eastern Pennsylvania.

There are several color phases or races of gyrfalcons. Those that venture into Canada and the United States are black, gray and white. At one time, it was thought the color phases were separate species, but now it is generally agreed they are races.

The gyrfalcon can be recognized by its long, pointed wings and great size. White gyrfalcons (*F. r. candicans*) are all white on the breast and mostly white above. The black gyrfalcon (*F. r. obsoletus*) is dark brown, often appearing to be all black when seen in the distance. Gray gyrfalcons (*F. r. uralensis*) are gray above and below. Both the black and gray phases of gyrfalcons have streaked or mottled underparts.

The gyrfalcon flies with fast, powerful wing beats, followed by an occasional sailing or soaring. It hovers above its prey, folds its wings and plunges down with astonishing speed, snatching a victim out of the air. With the victim held firmly in its sharp talons, the gyrfalcon seeks out a favorite eating place or devours the prey while continuing its flight.

Ptarmigans, Arctic grouse with feathered feet, are the favorite food of the gyrfalcons. Most of the time, ptarmigans are the only birds living in the frozen wastelands of the north. Sometimes these Arctic grouse move south in severe winters and the gyrfalcons are forced to move with them. The gyrfalcons will also prey on ducks and geese. Some observers of this great falcon report that these northern hawks feed on lemmings, small rodents that live in Arctic regions.

The gyrfalcon builds its aerie on rocky pinnacles close to the Arctic seacoasts. Often the aerie is placed just out of the reach of the icy water. Gyrfalcons breed in late April and early May, and the female lays four or five eggs. Both the female and tercel take turns incubating the eggs.

Swiftest of all the North American hawks is the peregrine (*Falco peregrinus anatum*). Although diminishing in numbers, this falcon has a wide range over North America. He breeds from the tree limit in the Arctic (the northernmost point where trees grow), southward through the United States to some of the southern states. Despite the fact that its range across the American continent extends from the Atlantic to the Pacific, the peregrine is rarely seen over the central plains.

He is a handsome bird, with blue-gray back and wings, a dark head and whitish underparts. His breast and belly have spots or streaks. A special feature of the peregrine is the black moustache or black bands extending from the base of the beak out to the cheeks.

Known as the "duck hawk," the peregrine likes to build his aerie high on the ledges of cliffs near large rivers or lakes. When I lived along the Hudson River above Tarrytown, New York, I often saw a pair of peregrines chasing ducks over the river. They had their aerie on the steep face of the Palisades on the western shore of the Hudson. And one year, I saw a peregrine hunting in the financial district of New York City. He preyed on the flocks of pigeons that eked out a living in the streets and parks of the city. When hunting, he would swoop down from a tall building, bind onto a pigeon, then mount swiftly up to some ledge on a skyscraper. He never came too close to the ground, nor did he try to knock the pigeon out of the air. It would have been too risky for the peregrine to go down into the streets to retrieve a pigeon.

The aerie of the peregrine is built with sticks and grass and lined with bark. Peregrines will occasionally move into an old bald eagle nest and patch it up with sticks and grass. The female lays three or four eggs, and both the tercel and female take turns with the incubating and feeding of the young peregrines.

Peregrines prey almost exclusively on birds, although they will eat rabbits, squirrels and other small mammals. Very few birds can escape this speedy hunter who can dart, twist, tumble and spin with unbelievable speed. Like the gyrfalcon, the peregrine flies with rapid wing beats, mounting high above its prey. Peregrines can glide and sail, but are not as adept at this as the broad-winged hawks.

In winter, most of the peregrines breeding north of the southern states migrate to warmer regions, usually the southern and Gulf states. The migration begins in October and the peregrines come down the flyways in company with other falcons, hawks, eagles and vultures. Since the peregrine is a bird hunter, he has been the target of countless farmers, hunters, and game bird-keepers. In recent years, the number of peregrines seen in migration has greatly diminished.

A western cousin to the peregrine is the prairie falcon (*Falco mexicanus*), a fierce hunter of the prairies. He resembles the peregrine in size and general appearance, but lacks the distinguished color and markings. The adult prairie falcon is light brown, but there are light and dark color phases in this species.

The prairie falcon hunts over the prairies, foothills and deserts west of the Great Plains. Its northern limit is southern Canada and it ranges as far south as southern

A fierce hunter, yet vital in the balance of nature

California and Mexico. Prairie falcons like to live high up and build their aeries on cliff ledges. The female lays her eggs, usually from two to five eggs, in April. Both the female and tercel take turns incubating the eggs and feeding the young.

The prairie falcon is a strong and fearless hunter, feeding on birds and small mammals. Included among the small mammals in the prairie falcon's diet are rats, gophers, ground squirrels, and mice. These fierce hunters have also been observed catching snakes. When hunting, the prairie falcon likes to fly over its victim, dart down and snatch up the victim. If chasing a large bird, the prairie falcon mounts above it and then plunges down in a stoop, knocking the bird out of the air.

The merlin or pigeon hawk (*Falco columbarius*) is next to the smallest of the falcons. There are two races of merlins in the United States: the eastern merlin (*F. c. columbarius*) and the western merlin (*F. c. bendirei*).

Eastern merlins are found from eastern Canada westward to the province of Manitoba. Their southern range extends down into the eastern part of the United States, east of the Great Plains. Western merlins breed in western Canada, southward through the United States into western and central Mexico.

Both the eastern and western merlins resemble peregrines, but are much smaller, about the size of a bluejay (ten to thirteen inches). The tercel is blue-gray on his upper parts, light underneath with streaks of black. His tail is black and tinged with white on the tip; there are also broad ash-gray bands on the tail. The female merlin is brown above and streaked with a rich brownish color below. Her tail is olive brown, with narrow buff-colored bars.

Merlins make their nests in trees, sometimes moving into an abandoned crow's nest. When they build a nest, it is usually made of twigs interwoven with some soft material, such as dead grass, inner tree bark or moss. The female lays four to five eggs and both parents help out with the incubating and feeding of the young merlins.

The merlin is primarily a bird eater, but will also hunt and eat squirrels, pocket gophers, young rabbits, lizards, scorpions, spiders, grasshoppers, small snakes, crickets, and beetles.

This small falcon likes to perch on telephone poles and trees, surveying the area below for prey. When it spies a bird or insect, the merlin darts down and snatches up the victim. The flight of the merlin is speedy and dashing, much like that of the bigger peregrine and prairie falcons. Merlins can overtake a swift, and the swift is one of our fastest birds.

Bold, fearless and very curious, the merlin will allow a human being to come very close. Merlins migrate down the flyways in the fall, and winter in the Gulf states, eastern Mexico, northern Mexico, northern South America, and the West Indies.

Smallest of the falcons is the little kestrel (*Falco sparverius*), often called the "sparrow hawk." This miniature falcon breeds over most of North America, southern Canada, and northern Mexico.

Both tercel and female are devoted parents

The kestrel is robin-size (nine to thirteen inches) and is shaped like a swallow. He is the prettiest of our falcons, with a blue-gray overcoat. His head is dark with black-and-white markings on the face. The best field mark of the kestrel, besides his small size, is the rufous tail. No other hawk or falcon has this color tail.

Kestrels build their nests in tree hollows or holes drilled by flickers and woodpeckers. The kestrel is not much of a housekeeper and doesn't do much with the nest in the way of lining. Often the female lays four or five eggs on the bare bottom of the hollow. Both female and tercel take turns incubating the eggs and feeding the baby kestrels.

The kestrel has a wide range in food tastes and eats small birds, small mammals, reptiles, frogs, toads, grasshoppers, cicadas, and beetles. This tiny falcon is an expert hunter, fast, dashing and as quick as lightning when it strikes its prey. Flying with fast wing beats, the kestrel scans the ground below for a victim. Then, hovering like a kingfisher for a few moments, the kestrel darts down and grabs the luckless rodent or insect.

Kestrels often indulge in playing with other birds. They will fly above, around and below a flock of birds. But it's all in fun and the kestrel doesn't attack any of the birds.

Look for the kestrel in open fields and near roadsides. You may see this small falcon coursing over a meadow in a tireless search for prey. Or you may see him perched on a telephone or electric wire along a road. In these days of television, you may see a kestrel perched atop a television antenna, patiently waiting for a fat insect to go by.

Kestrels migrate from their most northern range in winter, soaring down the flyways to the southern states. However, some kestrels live in city parks or on the fringes of cities during the winter. It is not unusual to see a kestrel chasing a sparrow or other small bird over the snow-covered fields of Central Park in New York City!

5

Accipiters

The Accipiters or "blue darters" are hawks with short, round wings and long tails. They are not as fast as the falcons, but are very agile hunters. Accipiters can twist and dart with surprising ability.

All of the blue darters have a distinct flight pattern. They fly with several wing beats, followed by a glide or sail. Like this: one, two, three, four, five—sail!

The blue darters are the brigands of the hawk world, preying on poultry and game birds. Unfortunately, by their poultry-raiding habits, the Accipiters bring harm and death to other hawks. Most farmers and hunters don't bother to identify a hawk. Any hawk flying or soaring over a poultry or game farm is a "chicken hawk" and out come the shotguns. Thus, many an innocent hawk is killed merely because he is a hawk.

Because of their fondness for poultry, only three states, Connecticut, Indiana and Michigan, offer some protection to the Accipiters. In these states, owners or tenants may kill an Accipiter only when the hawk is actually seen destroying poultry, game birds, or domestic animals. In other states, the Accipiters can be shot on sight.

I think there is too much ado about Accipiters killing poultry. I've been a farmer in Connecticut, New York, and Pennsylvania. And I've seen more poultry killed by weasels, skunks, foxes and stray dogs, than by hawks. I've also seen many chickens killed by disease and poor management!

Few will deny that the Accipiters prey on poultry. But these hawks also kill harmful rodents and insects, as well as help maintain the balance of nature. Certainly farmers and game birdkeepers have a right to protect their birds, but they also have a responsibility to protect the beneficial hawks and not blaze away at every hawk that soars over their farm. If an Accipiter is caught red-handed in the act of killing poultry or game birds, then he must forfeit his life. However, a poultry farmer or game birdkeeper should know the difference between an Accipiter and a broad-winged hawk, one of the most beneficial birds in the United States.

The largest of the Accipiters or blue darters is the goshawk (*Accipiter gentilis atricallus*). He breeds over most of Canada and the northeastern and middle Atlantic states, to as far west as Michigan.

Goshawks are bold, fierce hawks that speed down on their prey with deadly aim. The adult goshawk is a handsome hawk with a blue-gray back and pale gray breast. He has a black cap on his head and a white stripe over his eyes. The wings of this Accipiter are broad and round, and his tail is long and squared on the end.

Goshawks build their aeries in trees, using sticks and twigs for the framework and lining the nest with sprigs

Powerful wings carry the hawks aloft

of hemlock, fir or balsam. The female lays three or four eggs, and the young are hatched in four weeks.

When hunting, the goshawk flies low, darting here and there around the edges of woods. The goshawk can fly through the tangle of branches in a forest with ease. In medieval times, the goshawk was highly valued as a hunting hawk. It was called the "kitchen hawk," because of its prowess, and many a falconer added to his kitchen larder by hunting with a "gos." When the goshawk sights a victim, it darts down and snatches up the prey.

Most goshawks winter in their regular breeding range. However, a severe winter, with a lack of food, will bring the northern goshawks down into the more temperate states.

Next to the goshawk in size is the Cooper's hawk (*Accipiter cooperii*). This smaller Accipiter has the same blue-gray back as the goshawk. But his breast is rusty-red and his tail is rounded on the end. The Cooper's hawk ranges throughout most of the United States, extending his northern limits to Canada.

The Cooper's hawk builds its nest in pine and hardwood forests. A broad, flat structure, the nest is made with sticks and twigs and lined with bark and old feathers. The female lays four to five eggs and the incubation period is approximately twenty-five days.

Like his big relative, the goshawk, the Cooper's hawk has a lust for chickens and game birds. But he does hunt and eat rabbits, rats, mice, squirrels, lizards, frogs, toads, grasshoppers and beetles.

The flight of the Cooper's hawk is swift, agile and dashing; his short wings and long tail give him great control when winging in and out of branches in the deep woods. He surprises his prey with a sudden pounce.

While many Cooper's hawks remain in their breeding range during the winter, there is a large migration southward in the fall. They are seen migrating down the flyways, usually in company with ospreys and broad-winged hawks.

Smallest of the blue darters, but just as fierce, is the sharp-shinned hawk (*Accipiter striatus*). This Accipiter is a smaller version of the Cooper's hawk and is often mistaken for the larger hawk. The sharp-shinned hawk has the same blue-gray back and wings and his breast is rusty-red and barred. His tail, however, is square-tipped; that of the Cooper's hawk is rounded.

Sharp-shinned hawks are common throughout the United States and northward to Canada, as far as the tree limit. They are rare in the Mississippi valley, except during the migrations.

The sharp-shinned hawk builds its nest in pine forests or in woods that have both pine and hardwoods. Small twigs are used to build the nest, which has only a thin lining of pine bark and old feathers. The female lays four or five eggs, which are hatched in about three weeks.

A crafty hunter, the sharp-shinned hawk preys on poultry and pigeons. But it also hunts and eats rabbits, bats, rats, mice, frogs, toads, lizards, moths, beetles, and grasshoppers. When hunting, the sharp-shin flies low, skimming or hedge-hopping over bushes and low trees. Then, with a dash of speed, the sharp-shin darts down and snatches up its victim before it is even aware this hunter is around.

Sharp-shinned hawks begin to migrate southward in late August and continue through September. They can been seen coming down the flyways in large numbers, where they are frequently shot by farmers and hunters.

6

Buteos or Buzzard Hawks

The graceful soaring Buteos or buzzard hawks are the farmer's best friends. They are among the most beneficial birds in America, since the major portion of their food consists of harmful rodents and insects.

Buteos are the hawks most often seen "making lazy circles in the sky" on a hot summer day. They are big-bodied hawks with broad wings and short, wide tails. Buteos are slowpokes when compared with the falcons and Accipiters, but when it comes to soaring and riding the warm air currents, the Buteos have no peers.

The red-tailed hawk (*Buteo jamaicensis borealis*) is familiar in the eastern part of the United States. He ranges from the east coast to the Mississippi and north to Canada. He is a large, powerful hawk that is becoming scarce in certain areas of his range.

Adult eastern red-tails have light-colored bodies with dark bands across the belly. The tail is rufous on the upper part and white on the underside. When the red-tail banks in the sky, the reddish color of the tail is often seen as it shines through the white underpart. Most of the time, the red-tail holds his tail spread out like a fan while soaring, thus making it easier to identify him.

The eastern red-tail is a woodland hawk and builds its aerie high in oak and pine trees in the deep wood. The nest is flat and shallow, constructed from sticks and lined with strips of inner tree bark and sprigs of hemlock or pine. The female lays two eggs and the young are hatched within four weeks. Both parents help incubate the eggs and feed the young red-tails.

This big Buteo has a wide range of food: mice (house and field), rats, squirrels, gophers, prairie dogs, moles, skunks, weasels, bats, snakes, lizards, frogs, toads, grasshoppers, and other insects, and once in a while, the red-tail may catch a bird. The red-tail hunts either by soaring high above a wood or from a perch on a dead tree or pole. Male and female often hunt together, making a good team. Each hawk backs up the other in cornering the prey.

In flight, the red-tail is at its best when soaring in great wide circles. He climbs up, up into the sky, gradually gaining altitude, with his wings and tail outspread to take advantage of the warm air currents or thermals. Then, when he sees a victim, he plunges down in a steep nose dive that leaves one breathless!

Eastern red-tails migrate in the fall and spend the winter in the southern states and parts of northern Mexico. Beginning in September, the red-tails may be seen soaring down the flyways on a clear, cool day— making the most of the stiff breezes.

The western red-tailed hawk (*B. j. calurus*) lives west of the Mississippi, ranging as far north as western Canada and south to southern California. While this Buteo is rare

*The buteos or broad-winged hawks are among the
farmer's best friends*

in the upper Mississippi valley, he has been seen as far east as Minnesota.

Eastern and western red-tails are similar in body shape and general appearance. However, the western red-tail is darker, more of a red, and the markings on his breast are darker. There are also light-colored western red-tails and melanos, or black hawks.

The nesting habits of the western red-tails are similar to those of the eastern variety. But very often the western red-tail is forced to build its nest away from forests; for example, those living near prairies and deserts will nest in cacti, cottonwood and other trees. If near mountains or foothills, the western red-tail locates its aerie on cliffs or crags. The aerie is usually made with sticks and lined with dead grass, and the female lays from two to three eggs. Both the male and female help with the incubation and feeding of the young hawks.

This large western Buteo is a very beneficial hawk, feeding on ground squirrels, gophers, meadow mice, rabbits, snakes and prairie dogs. Unfortunately, not many farmers appreciate his value. Western red-tails hunt in the same manner as their eastern cousins and their flight pattern is similar. The western red-tail rarely molests small birds and may often be seen perched in company with a flock of songbirds!

Krider's hawk (*B. j krideri*) is considered to be a sub-species of the red-tailed hawk. This Buteo is not too common and is found mostly in the south-central part of Canada and the north-central United States. It has the same general body shape and markings as the eastern and western red-tail, but is much lighter, almost white in color. The face is mottled with reddish-brown streaks and the tail is a pale red.

While the Krider's hawk prefers to build its nest in trees, it will nest lower down on the prairies. The nest is a large one, built with sticks and dry prairie grass. The female lays three to five eggs and both parents assist with the incubation and feeding of the young hawks.

The food habits, hunting technique, and flight pattern of Krider's hawk are similar to those of the eastern red-tail. In the fall, this Buteo migrates south from its most northern range.

Harlan's hawk (*Buteo harlani*) is a black hawk of the western prairies. It breeds in the southern part of Alaska and the Canadian Northwest, southward to the prairies. At one time, it was thought this Buteo was a subspecies of the red-tailed hawk, but it is now generally accepted as a separate species.

There are two color phases in this species, a very dark and very light color, with both phases having spotted tails. Smaller than the red-tailed hawk, this Buteo is a daring hunter, feeding on mice, rats, ground squirrels and rabbits. When hunting, Harlan's hawk flies quickly and pounces on its prey.

Harlan's hawk is not very common and its range is restricted in all seasons. It migrates from September through November down the Mississippi valley to the Gulf states and northern Mexico.

The red-shouldered hawk (*B. lineatus*) ranges throughout southern Canada and the eastern United

States. It is a rare hawk on the prairies and deserts. In the east, the red-shouldered hawk is often called "the winter hawk," since it may be seen soaring high above a woods in winter. Red-shouldered hawks prefer moist woodlands for their breeding and hunting grounds.

Red-shouldered hawks have rufous shoulders, light red underparts and a tail that is banded with narrow strips of white. A field mark for the red-shouldered hawk is the "light panes" or "windows" near the shoulder-end of the wings, seen when this hawk is soaring and the light strikes the "windows."

Since the red-shouldered hawk is a woodland hawk, it builds its nest in tall trees in dense forests. New nests are built each year and are constructed from sticks and lined with inner tree bark, dry leaves, moss, lichens, down, old feathers, and sprigs of evergreens. Red-shouldered hawks are very competitive hunters and will not build their aeries near any other hawks of their species. The female lays three to four eggs and both parents take turns incubating the eggs, which hatch in about four weeks.

This big woodland Buteo is a highly beneficial hawk, feeding on mice, rats, squirrels, snakes, grasshoppers, moths, frogs, and occasionally fish. When hunting, the red-shouldered hawk glides rapidly along on stiff wings, skimming over the tops of trees and bushes. It slips up on its victim, snatching it from a tree or off the ground with a quick pounce.

Like the other Buteos, the red-shouldered hawk is a slow flier, but once it mounts to the sky and begins to

*Talons outstretched, the red-shouldered hawk
pounces on a hapless rodent*

soar, it changes into a graceful aerialist. Many red-shouldered hawks remain in the north during the winter, staying well below the very cold regions. The majority, however, ride the winds south in the middle of September and October.

Another familiar Buteo is the chunky broad-winged hawk (*Buteo platypterus*), a shy and retiring hawk of the deep woods. Broad-wings breed in the more arid forests of western Canada, eastward to the Atlantic coast and south to the Gulf states and Texas.

The broad-wing is dark brown on his upper parts, with a white throat and brown bars on the underparts. His tail is barred with three black and three white bands. Smaller than the other Buteos, this woodland Buteo has broad wings that are whitish and tipped with brown.

Broad-wings are not very particular when it comes to building a nest. The nest is small and poorly-constructed, usually of sticks, and sparsely lined with bark, sprigs of evergreens and green leaves. In summer, fresh green leaves help to cool the nest. The female lays two eggs and both parents help incubate them.

The broad-wing is a beneficial hawk, preying on mice, rats, shrews, rabbits, grasshoppers, and other harmful insects. It likes to hunt from a perch on dead trees or telephone poles, where it can watch for victims. When a victim is sighted, the broad-wing jumps up off the perch and darts down with great speed, snatching up the prey.

In a straight flight, the broad-wing seems sluggish and slow. But just let this Buteo mount to the sky and catch onto a thermal, and a graceful soaring and gliding display can be seen.

These shy hawks migrate in large flocks, beginning at the end of August and continuing through October. They can be depended upon to show up in great numbers over the various hawk observation points. Dr. Maurice Broun, Curator of the Hawk Mountain Sanctuary, once reported that more than 10,000 broad-winged hawks passed over Hawk Mountain in one day!

While I can't claim to have seen this many broad-wings in one day, I have seen flocks of several hundred soaring along. And clumsy though the broad-wing may seem alongside a falcon, there is something inspiring about a regiment of broad-wings soaring down the flyways.

Out on the Great Plains, another Buteo rides the thermals. This is Swainson's hawk (*B. swainsoni*), breeding in most of the western states. It is a hawk with light plumage; the throat is pure white and the chest has a band of dull brown. The tail is mostly gray with many thin bands of a darker color.

Swainson's hawk makes its nest in low trees, usually cottonwoods, box elders and willows. The nest is built with sticks, interwoven with dead grass and weeds. It is lined with inner tree bark and fresh green leaves. The female lays two to four eggs and both parents help with the incubation.

This Buteo of the plains is a beneficial hawk, feeding on mice, rats, rabbits, gophers, locusts, and grasshoppers. Swainson's hawk seems awkward and heavy in flight, but it is a graceful soarer. Like the broad-wings, these west-ern Buteos gather in large flocks late in August. They soar and wheel overhead, waiting for a strong breeze to carry them south to Central America and northern South America.

A Buteo of the open fields in the eastern part of the United States is the American rough-legged hawk (*B. lagopus s. johannis*). This hawk breeds in northern Canada to the tree limit and winters in the United States.

Rough-legs have longer wings and tails than any other Buteo. The tail is mostly white with a black band at the tip. Its head is white, streaked with dark bars. Rough-legs have white rumps and may be confused with the harrier or marsh hawk, which has a white rump patch. The leg shanks of the rough-legged hawk are feathered. There are light and dark phases in this species.

The rough-leg builds its nest on cliff ledges, usually of sticks and lined with dead grass, hay, moss, down, and old feathers. Three to four eggs are laid and the incuba-tion period is approximately four weeks.

Rough-legs rarely attack birds, but prey largely on mice, rats, weasels, rabbits, large insects, and lizards. When hunting, the rough-leg flaps and sails close to the ground, quartering a field like a hunting dog. Then he hovers for a few minutes, and when he sees a victim, plunges swiftly down and snatches up the prey. The rough-leg is the only eastern Buteo that hovers.

The rough-leg, like the other Buteos, is slow and awkward in a straight flight, but a magnificent soarer when riding the thermals. As he soars, the rough-leg

*Soon the baby hawks will learn to do their
own hunting*

spreads out his wings, with the tips tilted upward. And as he gains altitude, this Buteo teeters on the thermals, rising higher and higher until he becomes a small speck in the sky.

Unfortunately, the rough-leg often soars over the lands of hostile farmers and game birdkeepers. When he appears, the shotguns are dragged out and this harmless Buteo is blasted out of the sky.

Powerful, regal, the ferruginous hawk (*B. regalis*) is another Buteo of the west. He ranges from southern Canada, southward into the western part of the United States. As his name implies, this Buteo is a rusty-iron color on the upper parts and white underneath. His tail is white or gray and has no bars or bands. There are light and dark phases among the ferruginous hawks.

Ferruginous hawks nest in trees, building their nests with large sticks and lining them with grass and strips of inner tree bark. Both the male and female help to incubate the three or four eggs. Young ferruginous hawks are hatched out in four weeks and keep both parents busy hunting and bringing back food.

A beneficial hawk, the ferruginous hawk feeds on mice, rats, gophers, snakes, and rabbits. He is a great help to wheat farmers, since he preys on gophers. As any wheat farmer knows, the gopher can eat a bushel of wheat in one season. Ferruginous hawks usually hunt in pairs, one hawk flying overhead, the other skimming low over the ground. This teamwork enables them to corner and run down rabbits and gophers.

Ferruginous hawks spend a lot of time perching on posts or tree stumps. They are not great fliers, but, like the other Buteos, can soar for miles with hardly a wing beat. Most of these Buteos winter in the northern part of the western states, south to Mexico.

The smallest of the Buteos is the crow-size short-tailed hawk (*B. brachyurus*), a South American hawk that rarely comes north of southern Florida. Short-tailed hawks have two color phases: white and black.

Short-tails make their nests with sticks and line them with Spanish moss. The female lays from one to three eggs. The food of this rare hawk consists of mice, rats, frogs, lizards, and small snakes. It is an expert soarer and congregates in the sky with kites and vultures.

All of the Buteos play a major role in the extermination of harmful insects and rodents. Rarely, if ever, do they prey on game birds or poultry. Yet, farmers and game birdkeepers view them with suspicion and reach for their shotguns. This is a very short-sighted action; farmers, especially, need all the help they can get to eliminate insects and rodents.

7

Harrier, Caracara and Osprey

Skimming low over coastal and inland marshes, the harrier or marsh hawk (*circus cyaneus hudsonius*) is an expert hunter. He is a large hawk with a long tail and wings, brown breast and a white patch on his rump.

The harrier breeds over a wide range in the United States, Canada and southern Alaska. While he prefers marshes and swamps, he is also found hunting over plains and prairies.

Harriers build their nests near the ground in marshes and cut-over land. The nest is built with sticks, weeds and cattail stems. Most of the work in building the nest is done by the female, who lays four to six eggs. Young harriers hatch in approximately three weeks.

A careful and relentless hunter, the harrier is the scourge of the meadow mice. He also feeds on frogs, snakes, and insects—and will occasionally prey on poultry and water fowl. But the harrier does more good than harm and doesn't deserve the persecution it receives from farmers and hunters.

When hunting, the harrier sails low over the marsh or plains, quartering the area carefully, with perfect control of his flight. Then, when he sees a victim, he stops suddenly and drops down with great speed. In flight, the wings of the harrier are held up from the horizontal, in a dihedral angle. And as he wheels away from you, his white rump badge is visible.

Harriers living in the north begin their fall migration early in September, soaring down the flyways to the southern states. Some remain in the coastal marshes south of New England and may be seen hunting over the frosty swamps.

Audubon's caracara (*Polyborus cheriway auduboni*) is a northern race of a South American hawk. Oddly enough, it is a hawk with the food habits of a vulture. Once plentiful, when Audubon was painting his *Birds of America*, the caracara is now restricted to a small range. It is seen in southern Texas, parts of Arizona and in the Kissimmee Plains of central Florida. The Kissimmee Plains, north of Lake Okeechobee, are low grassy lands with countless small ponds and streams. They are the favorite hunting grounds of many hawks and vultures.

The caracara is an ungainly hawk, with a long neck and legs. Its long legs permit the caracara to walk or run on the ground. This vulture-hawk is brown and has a white tail rimmed with black. There is a crest that flares up from the top of the head, and the face is red. The caracara has an eaglelike beak and the general posture of a bald eagle.

Even though the caracara prefers to join the vultures in their grisly feasts, he will occasionally hunt live prey. Included in his diet are fish, rodents, snakes, amphibians, and insects. In flight, the caracara resembles the harrier

The osprey is one of nature's expert fishermen

sailing, twisting, rising and falling as he searches for food.

This strange hawk makes its nest in the cabbage palmetto tree. The nest is made of twigs and lined with the fruit and leaves of the palmetto. There are usually two to three eggs and both the male and female help with the incubation.

Big, eaglelike and an expert fisherman, the osprey (*Pandion haliaetus carolinensis*) competes with fishermen up and down the Atlantic coast. He will be found inland, but always near large bodies of water. This great fish hawk breeds as far north as northern Canada and Alaska, and southward through the United States into the Gulf of Mexico and northern Mexico.

The osprey is a large hawk with a wingspread measuring four and a half to five feet. His upper parts are dark brown or black and the underparts are white. The head is white with a black patch.

Ospreys are not too particular about where they build their nests. If tall trees are nearby, the aerie will be built on a strong branch. But in the absence of tall trees, the osprey will not hesitate to place the aerie on the crossbars of a telephone or electric line pole.

The big osprey aeries on telephone or electric line poles cause headaches among the utility companies. Sometimes the metal junk with which the osprey lines the nest touches a live wire and causes a short circuit. The result is an electrocuted osprey and a black-out for the local home owners.

Some utility companies try to drive away the ospreys, others adopt another policy. I saw a good example of this action when I lived in Ocean City, New Jersey. A few miles west of Ocean City, a large osprey aerie sits atop the crossbar of an abandoned line pole. The utility company simply gave it to the ospreys. The top of the pole is sawed off and the aerie rests upon the one remaining crossbar. As far as the utility company is concerned, the ospreys can cart as much junk up to their aerie as they wish. There's no danger of a short circuit, since the lines are strung around the aerie on other poles.

The osprey's aerie is usually built with large sticks, some of them three feet long and as thick as your wrist. Most nests are lined with paper, cardboard, roofing material, cattail reeds and whatever else strikes the osprey's fancy. The female lays three eggs and does all of the incubating. However, the male hunts and brings back food for the female while she sits on the eggs.

Ospreys feed on fresh and salt water fish. They prefer to catch live fish, but will pick up a dead fish that is fresh. The osprey is not a scavenger in the same sense as the bald eagle, however. In hunting, the osprey sails over the water with a gull-like hook or curve to his wings. He flies thirty to seventy-five feet above the water, his keen eyes watching for signs of fish. He will hover, beating his wings rapidly, and then when he sees a fish, plummet down on half-folded wings. He strikes the water with his chest, sending up a spray of water. Grasping the fish by the head, he rises heavily out of the water, then flies up to a favorite perch or to the aerie to devour his catch.

Whenever a bald eagle lives in the vicinity of an osprey, you can expect a running feud. The bald eagle is the robber king of the air. He seems to take great delight in bullying and robbing the hard-working osprey.

I've seen a bald eagle steal a fish from an osprey. The robbery occurred just off Stony Point, a rugged peak in the Hudson river below Peekskill, New York. You may recall that during the Revolutionary War the British held the Point. Doubtless, the British garrison atop Stony Point witnessed battles between bald eagles and ospreys. That is, they did until a "fox" and "eagle" decided to take Stony Point away from them. The "fox" was General Washington, and the "eagle" was "Mad" Anthony Wayne.

But to return to the bald eagle and osprey affair that I witnessed. I sat on the steep slope of Stony Point watching an osprey flying up the river. He hovered over the water just below me, then plunged down with a big splash. Up he came with a large fish. Clutching the fish by the head, he winged toward a dead tree to my right. But he never reached the tree. Suddenly a bald eagle hurtled off Stony Point and flew straight at the osprey.

Changing course, the osprey headed down the river with the eagle close on his tail. Up mounted the eagle; then, with talons outstretched, he dove at the osprey. Still holding onto his fish, the osprey side-slipped away from the eagle and tried to out-fly the eagle. But the eagle thudded into the osprey, jarring him off his course. Again and again the eagle struck until the osprey finally dropped the fish and rolled over to do battle. But the eagle had accomplished what he set out to do, force the osprey to drop the fish. Ignoring the osprey, who now bristled with anger, the eagle nose-dived down and retrieved the fish from the rocks below. Then, with mighty wing beats, he flew up the river with his booty.

Screaming angry protests, the osprey flew after the retreating eagle. But the eagle was too fast and the osprey gave up the chase. He swung out over the river, heading for the western shore where he must have decided to fish as far away as possible from the pirating bald eagle.

Most ospreys winter in the southern United States, and they begin to migrate in late August and early September. These big fish hawks are often seen soaring down the flyways along with other hawks.

8

Eagles

Perched high on a mountain crag or soaring down a windy canyon, the eagle is a majestic bird, a powerful lord of the sky. This big cousin of the lesser hawks once ruled the skies from the Atlantic to the Pacific. Now the eagles are becoming scarce. The bald eagle, in particular, has declined alarmingly in the last quarter of a century.

The bald eagle (*Haliaeetus leucocephalus*) is a native American eagle and the national emblem of the United States. There are two races of bald eagle in North America: the northern bald eagle (*H. l. washingtoniensis*) and the southern bald eagle (*H. l. leucocephalus*). The main difference between the two races is the size— the northern race being the larger of the two.

Ranging from the Arctic southward and eastward to the Great Lakes and northeastern states, the northern bald eagle is a huge bird with a wingspread over seven feet. He is not bald or devoid of feathers on the head as, for example, the turkey vulture. Both the male and female bald eagles have white heads and tails. The rest of the plumage is dark brown. Young bald eagles are

87

slow to acquire the white head and may be several years old before they can display the famous white head of their parents.

Bald eagles build large aeries with sticks, weeds, cornstalks, and rubbish. The largest bald eagle aerie ever discovered was the "great nest" near Vermilion, Ohio. It is believed that this aerie was started in 1890 and succeeding generations of eagles kept adding to it. Just before it was destroyed by a severe storm, this aerie was twelve feet high and eight and a half feet wide!

The female lays one to three eggs and both parents incubate the eggs. Young eaglets appear in five weeks and the male and female are kept busy feeding the hungry babies. Eaglets are slow growers when compared with the young of the lesser hawks.

While the bald eagle is primarily a scavenger, feeding on dead or nearly-dead fish, he will also hunt crows, rats, small snakes, rabbits, and squirrels. Bald eagles have been accused of preying on poultry, game fish, and young domestic animals. For instance, the salmon-fishing industries claim the bald eagles in the northwest prey on spawning salmon. However, this claim doesn't fit in with the food habits of this eagle. He is not a fisherman in the same sense as an osprey, but prefers to pick up dead or expiring fish. And when he doesn't find any fish, he turns to birds and small mammals.

The bald eagle is very impressive as he flies with slow, powerful wing beats. He holds his wings out flat when soaring. The flat position of the bald eagle's wings helps to distinguish him from the eaglelike osprey, who soars

Hungry baby hawks keep their parents searching for food

with wings hooked or curved like those of a gull. An accomplished aerialist, the bald eagle can rush down toward his prey in a steep nose dive and then pounce on the victim.

When the winters up north are severe and the ice jams the lakes and rivers, bald eagles move south where they can find fish. On several occasions, when I lived along the Hudson river, I saw bald eagles riding down the river on big cakes of ice. Generally, the northern bald eagle migrates just south of the deep-freeze areas.

The southern bald eagle, although smaller than his northern kin, has similar habits. He ranges north to the Carolinas, but has been observed as far north as southern New England.

Florida is "bald eagle land" and the greatest number of aeries are to be found in that state. Most of the aeries are in Pinellos and Brevard counties, placed high in pine trees. The aeries are built with large sticks and rubbish. One to two eggs are laid and the incubation period is close to that of the northern race. Both parents incubate the eggs and feed the eaglets.

Southern bald eagles have the same hunting and food habits as the northern variety. Some southern farmers, however, maintain that bald eagles raid the chicken yards and occasionally make off with a young lamb. Just how true this accusation may be is difficult to say, since bald eagles are protected and can't be killed—which fact prevents an examination of their stomachs for traces of prey.

When Congress selected the bald eagle to be the national emblem in 1782, there were some objectors. Benjamin Franklin was one. Franklin called the bald eagle a thief and scavenger, stating that the golden eagle was a nobler eagle. True, the bald eagle is a thief and scavenger and his habits are less noble than those of the golden eagle. But these traits in no way detract from his majesty and power. And Franklin overlooked the fact that the bald eagle is an American eagle—"home bred," so to say, and that the golden eagle is a western race of an European eagle.

Ornithologists have become alarmed over the decline of the bald eagle in the United States. Plume hunters, fishermen, farmers, and hunters have all helped to reduce the bald eagle population. But, in the east, another factor is responsible for the bald eagle's decline. This is the pollution of the waters from which the bald eagle takes fish.

The federal government has taken steps to prevent the shooting and capture of eagles. The Congressional Act of 1940 recognized the status of the bald eagle as a national emblem and a declining species. This act forbids the killing or taking of bald eagles within the United States.

But unless something is done to stop the pollution of waters, the bald eagle will continue to decline. This regal bird will soon be added to the naturalist's "Hall of Infamy"—the list of birds and mammals slaughtered into extinction. The list is getting longer and includes the ivory-billed woodpecker, heath hen, passenger pigeon, California condor and others.

Once bald eagles and their aeries were seen in large numbers in New Jersey. But in 1959, only eight aeries were known to exist in that state. And a year or two ago, only ten adult and immature bald eagles were sighted in the Garden State.

Observers in New Jersey reported that, while bald eagles were laying eggs and incubating them, no eaglets have appeared for more than three years! Why? Ornithologists blame the increased use of insecticides and other chemicals in the rivers, lakes and streams. They believe the eagles are made sterile by eating fish poisoned by chemicals.

Recently, a hopeful note was sounded in New Jersey. The New Jersey Audubon Society cautiously stated that bald eagles were making a slight comeback in New Jersey. In 1961, a record group, ten bald eagles and one golden eagle, was seen at the Brigantine National Wildlife Refuge near Atlantic City. The location of the eagles and their aeries is a closely guarded secret.

Also on the decline is the golden eagle (*Aquila chrysaetos*), the monarch of the west. This mighty hunter breeds in the Rocky Mountains, especially in California, and is found in limited numbers in the Appalachian Mountains on the east coast. He is dark brown, often appearing to be all black when seen in the distance. But when seen close up—and the sun or light strikes him—the observer often catches sight of the famous crown of golden hackles. Golden eagles have feathers

*Strong and courageous, the golden eagle is truly
a lord of the sky*

on their legs, down to the talons, while the bald eagles have none on their shanks.

The golden eagle nests high on rocky cliffs. It builds a large aerie with sticks, roots, and reeds, lining the structure with bark and leaves. The female lays two eggs and does all the incubating. While the male scorns "housework," he does hunt and bring food to the female while she incubates the eggs.

Golden eagles are skilled hunters, working in pairs to corner their prey. They have great courage and will not hesitate to attack large mammals and poisonous snakes. Snakes, birds, gophers, jackrabbits, prairie dogs, young deer and antelope, lambs of the mountain sheep, fox—all are the prey of this fierce eagle. He has a lofty, soaring flight, riding high on the thermals with wings stretched out flat like those of the bald eagle. Wheeling and sailing, he searches the land below for a victim; then, partially folding his great wings, he speeds down in a steep nose dive. He quickly levels off and drops on the victim with a mighty pounce.

It is true that this powerful eagle is a marauder, occasionally making off with poultry and young farm animals. But he does lend a hand to the farmers and ranchers. For every lamb or chicken he steals, he kills at least ten harmful rodents. Unfortunately, the farmers and ranchers do not accept this and the yellow-eyed king of the air is persecuted and shot down by hunters in airplanes. Actually, the small numbers of poultry and livestock taken by this eagle do not warrant his wholesale destruction. Like all wild creatures, he takes his food where he finds it.

Fortunately for the golden eagle, President Kennedy signed a new law that prohibits shooting golden eagles without a license. The law, signed in October of 1962, specifies that such licenses will be issued by the Interior Department for farmers in areas where the golden eagle is found to be preying on livestock.

Golden eagles are usually year-round residents, except in the extreme northern parts of their range. They are occasionally seen migrating down the Appalachian flyways. It is a great day for the hawk watchers when they spot a golden eagle soaring along on the winds, his wings held horizontal, the tips of the primaries reaching upward. He is the mightiest of all the hawks, the king of the air!

9

Kites

Slim, graceful and swallowlike, the kites are among our rare birds. They are elegant hawks with great buoyancy and mobility as they hover, sail, dip, and lift in the breeze like a paper kite bobbing aloft on a windy March day. Once these dapper hawks bred over a wide range in the United States. Now they are restricted to a small area in the Gulf states and southern California.

The swallow-tailed kite (*Elanoides forficatus forficatus*) looks like an oversized swallow. He has a white head, neck and underparts and his back and wings are black. His most distinguishing feature is a long black forked tail.

Swallow-tails build their nests with sticks and Spanish moss and place them high in trees in cypress swamps. There are usually two eggs which are incubated by both parents. Known as the "snake hawk," the swallow-tail preys on small snakes, lizards, amphibians and insects. Sometimes visitors to the Everglades are treated to the sight of a swallow-tail swooping down and plucking a snake off a tree limb.

The flight of the swallow-tail is erratic, rushing here and there, with sure wing strokes and steady whipping of the forked tail. When hunting, the swallow-tail "kites" in the air, teetering, side-slipping—then swooping down to snatch up its victim. Holding the prey in its talons, the swallow-tail continues its erratic flight, eating as it goes.

Most swallow-tails migrate to South America in the winter, although some remain in southern Florida. Plume hunters and hawk killers have taken their toll and this beautiful hawk is becoming a rare species. In Audubon's day, he ranged from eastern Minnesota south to the Gulf states. Today, you are fortunate to see him in the river swamps of Florida and Louisiana.

Smaller than the swallow-tail, but just as agile, is the Mississippi kite (*Ictinia misisippiensis*)—a slim hawk that once ranged over the central United States. Now its breeding range is limited to the Gulf states, with a few of these hawks living as far north as Kansas and southern Missouri.

The Mississippi kite is dark gray above and light gray below, with a pearl-gray head. This gray-clad kite builds its nest in the top of a tall tree, using sticks for the framework and lining the nest with fresh green leaves. The female lays one or two eggs and is assisted in the incubation by the male.

Like the swallow-tailed kite, the Mississippi kite feeds on the wing, hunting grasshoppers, locusts, cicadas, beetles, and other insects. It hunts carefully, hovering in the air, swinging this way and that, then swooping down on its prey. Holding the victim in its talons, the Mississippi kite eats as it flies. Most of these kites remain in their breeding and hunting grounds all year round.

Falcon-shaped, with long, pointed wings and long tail, the white-tailed kite (*Elanus leucurus majusculus*) is a rare, but beneficial hawk. He once was common in all of the Gulf states, but is now found in southern Texas and California. He lives close to rivers, streams and marshes.

The white-tailed kite is light-colored, pale gray on the body and whitish on the head and tail. In the distance, he seems to be all white, but when nearby, the dark shoulders stand out. He has a well-rounded tail.

White-tails build their nests in trees, constructing them from sticks, grass, straw, weed stems, and Spanish moss. The female lays four to five eggs and both parents take turns incubating them. These helpful hawks hunt mice, rats, gophers, ground squirrels, small snakes, grasshoppers, frogs, and toads. They hunt by "kiting" or teetering aloft, legs dangling downward. When the white-tail spots a victim, he drops down, snatches up the prey, and devours it on the wing.

The flight of the white-tail is light and graceful, with rapid wing beats. As it flies, the white-tail holds its wings up in a slight hook, similar to that of the osprey, but not as pronounced. Winging along, the white-tail courses here and there like a kestrel. These kites are not migrants, but stay in their restricted range throughout the year.

Rarest of the kites is the everglade kite (*Rostrhamus sociabilis plumbeus*), a slow-flying hawk seen over a small area of the southern Everglades in Florida. He is a dark hawk with a white patch at the base of his tail. His beak and legs are bright orange and his wings are the broadest of the kites.

The everglade kite has been pushed to the brink of extinction by hunters and a scarcity of food. He is a specialist when it comes to food, preying exclusively on the fresh water snail (*Ampullaria depressa*). But various parts of the Everglades have been drained, thus reducing the snail population to a point where the everglade kite is hard pressed to find food.

Other forms of wildlife have been affected by the changes wrought by man and Nature in the Everglades. The 1,500,000 acres of unique wilderness that make up the Everglades are a natural paradise. Yet, even in this natural paradise, some birds, mammals and reptiles find it difficult to survive. Florida state conservationists and other interested groups are constantly seeking ways to preserve the wildlife in this fascinating region. So far, they have not managed to stem the decline of the everglade kite. Between the scarcity of food and the hawk hunters, this kite seems to be waging a losing battle for survival.

In hunting the fresh water snail, the everglade kite sails and hovers, quartering like a harrier. It flies low, hanging still in the air for a few minutes, then drops down when it sees a snail. Gripping the snail in its talons, the everglade kite flies up to a favorite eating place and extracts the snail from the shell with its long, hooked beak. After the snail is taken out, the unbroken shell is dropped to the ground or water. As far as it can be determined, this kite eats nothing else.

When not hunting, the everglade kite meanders here and there, with slow, lazy wing beats. Or it may be seen "kiting" on high, hovering, tippling, and rising on the wind. Unless this rare kite changes its food habits—or the Florida conservationists find some way to increase the snail supply—future generations of Americans will see the everglade kite only in bird books or museums.

10

Vultures

Wheeling high above the earth—with keen eyes scanning the landscape below—soar the vultures. They are the "sanitation department" of the bird world, quickly dropping out of the sky onto any carrion sighted from above. Vultures belong to the same order as the hawks, falcons, eagles, kites and osprey. But, as scavengers and carrion-eaters, they are specialized hawks.

Vultures have long been regarded as birds of ill omen, harbingers of death. Superstitious people shudder when these carrion-eaters soar overhead. To be sure, the vulture is concerned with death, for he is either searching for carrion—circling on high—or he is feeding on the carcasses of mammals, birds or reptiles. Gruesome though his task may be, the vulture is a beneficial bird.

Two races of vultures are commonly seen over the United States: the turkey vulture (*Cathartes aura*) and black vulture (*Coragyps stratus*). Both races are similar in appearance and habits.

The turkey vulture is eagle-size, with a wingspread of six feet. He is found soaring and wheeling over most of the United States and into northern Mexico. In the sky he appears to be dark brown or black, with a rounded tail. When seen close up, he has a naked red head and neck, long beak and turkeylike feet.

This ungainly carrion-eater makes little or no attempt to build a nest, but utilizes cliff ledges, caves, hollow logs, even empty barns or out-buildings, for its home. Seldom does the turkey vulture do any more in the way of housekeeping than to line the bottom of the aerie with dead leaves or rotten wood. The female lays two eggs and both parents help with the incubation.

Since the turkey vulture is not a hunter of live prey, he must spend many hours soaring overhead, constantly searching for carrion. On the ground, he is awkward and clumsy, hopping over to his victims, which include the carcasses of birds, mammals, reptiles and amphibians. He is equally as awkward when he tries to take off from the ground, tipping his naked head forward, then shoving off with his turkeylike feet and at the same time flapping his great wings.

But aloft on the thermals, with his wings held up from the horizontal, the turkey vulture soars and wheels with great buoyancy. When the wind is strong, the tips of the primaries spread apart, like long fingers reaching skyward. And through binoculars, the red head can be seen moving from side to side as the eternal search for food goes on.

The turkey vulture is rarely the target of the hawk hunters, although, doubtless, hunters have taken potshots at him. Even among the hawk hunters, there seems to be an acceptance of the vultures and their revolting work.

Turkey vultures are to be seen in winter, soaring and circling as they search for carrion. But when the winters are severe and the snow flies fast, they are forced to migrate southward, where they have a better chance to find food.

The black vulture is smaller than the turkey vulture, with a wingspread under five feet. He is all black and his head and neck are featherless. However, he has a black head and neck, whereas the turkey vulture has a red head and neck. His tail is short and square. Black vultures breed over most of the southeastern United States, often ranging as far north as Ohio and southern Illinois, and as far west as Texas.

Like his red-headed relative, the black vulture dispenses with nest-building and utilizes hollow stumps, caves, and depressions in the ground. The two eggs laid on the bare floor of the cave or hollow stump are incubated by both parents. Black vultures flock around a carcass, hissing and fighting with each other or with any turkey vultures or eagles that may decide to join the feast.

Despite his awkwardness on the ground, the black vulture is a graceful flier, soaring and wheeling for miles and miles. But he is not as expert a soarer as the turkey vulture. He usually flies with several wing beats, followed by a glide and, unlike the turkey vulture, holds his wings out flat, like those of an eagle.

Rarest of all the daytime birds of prey is the giant California condor (*Gymnogyps californianus*), a vulture that lives among the steep and rocky canyons of

Ugly though he may be, the vulture is an important member of nature's "sanitation department"

southern California. This nearly-extinct vulture is the largest of all the hawks, with a wingspread close to ten feet. He seems like a primitive bird from the dim Ice Age. In fact, the California condor is a direct descendant of an Ice Age bird called *Teratornis,* a Pterodactyl-like bird that had a twelve-foot wingspread.

Not many people have seen the California condor in his native habitat. It is estimated that not more than sixty of these great vultures live in the United States. The last-known nests are in the Sespe Wildlife Preserve in southern California. Their location is a closely-guarded secret and a special license must be procured just to enter the region where these birds might be found.

The California condor is a dark bird with a bright-colored head. This big carrion-eater does not build any nest and the female lays one egg on the bare floor of a cave or on a rocky ledge. It is believed that the California condor did not recently start down the road to extinction, but is a species that has been on its way out for more than a thousand years. One of the factors contributing to the decline of this primitive vulture is that the female lays only one egg every other season.

Master of the art of soaring, the California condor flies with powerful and sweeping wing beats, then sails for miles and miles, tacking this way and that. When he catches onto a thermal, he rises higher and higher, great wings spread out, until he seems to disappear into space. For those fortunate enough to see it, the long sailing flight of the California condor is a sight to remember.

II

Hawk Mountain Sanctuary

Each year, thousands of men, women and children gather to watch the hawk migrations. In the mountains, on the plains and along the coasts, the hawk watchers aim their binoculars at the soaring hawks.

There are many good hawk observation posts throughout the country, some well-known, others known but to a few. It is in the northeastern states, however, that hawk watching has the most followers. Among the better known observation posts in the northeast are Wantasquet mountain in Vermont, Waggoner's Gap and Hawk Mountain in Pennsylvania, Point Pelee in Ontario, Fisher's Island in Long Island Sound and Cape May Point in New Jersey.

But the most famous hawk observation site is the craggy top of Hawk Mountain, near Hamburg, Pennsylvania. Here, with a magnificent view of the Blue Mountains—called Kittatinny or "endless mountain"—the hawk watchers gather for the autumnal migration of the hawks.

Hawk Mountain Sanctuary is the Mecca for hawk enthusiasts. Watchers from many states and more than a dozen foreign countries make an annual pilgrimage to the Sanctuary. It is not unusual to meet hawk fanciers from Canada, England, Germany, Japan, India, and the Scandinavian countries clustered on the mountaintop, binoculars in hand, eagerly watching the soaring hawks.

On a crisp autumn day, you will see young and old hiking up the winding, stony trail to the Lookout, the rocky pinnacle of Hawk Mountain. I have seen women with babies, boys and girls of all ages and old-timers, well into and beyond their seventies, paying tribute to the lords of the sky.

The Sanctuary consists of 1,418 acres of Pennsylvania forest land, north of Hamburg, Pennsylvania. Hemlocks, white oaks, birches, white pines and dogwoods canopy the steep slope of the mountain. Lush stands of laurel and rhododendron are everywhere. The Sanctuary teems with wildlife. Deer, raccoon, squirrel, chipmunk, weasel, and skunk roam unmolested over the Sanctuary grounds. Overhead in the treetops are owls, songbirds, and woodpeckers.

Primarily, the Sanctuary is dedicated to the conservation and protection of all wildlife. But it is in the field of hawk conservation that the Sanctuary and its staff have made the greatest contributions. Once the rocky crest of Hawk Mountain was dotted with hawk killers. In fact, until recently, there were eleven major hawk shooting sites along the Kittatinny range, from Windgap to Bethel. Thousands of hawks were shot out of the skies above the "endless mountain." Pennsylvania's "bloody ridges" are what Dr. Maurice Broun, Curator of the Hawk Mountain Sanctuary, has so aptly called them.

*Over the "lookout" on Hawk Mountain soar the
falcons, hawks and eagles*

Before the Sanctuary was established in 1934, men and boys climbed up to the top of Hawk Mountain and the nearby ridges to shoot the migrating hawks. These hawk killers came from the coal regions to the north, the farm country to the west and up from the cities in the south. They were a trigger-happy brand of hunter, shooting at any bird or animal. Conservation and game laws meant nothing to them, especially when it came to a hawk. A hawk was a hawk, according to these hunters. It was a "mean" bird and deserved to be killed. The fact that most of the hawks they slew were on Pennsylvania's protected bird list made no impression. A hawk was *still* a hawk!

These hawk hunters (and they still exist) refuse to admit that hawks are beneficial birds. And they fiercely resent any interference with their so-called "sport." When pinned down for a good reason why they kill hawks, the stock answer is, "All predatory creatures should be killed." This, of course, is nonsense. If it were true, then all human beings should be killed. For man is the most predatory creature of all.

Dr. Broun and the Hawk Mountain Sanctuary have spent years trying to educate the public to the value of hawks and the need to protect them. These have been years of struggle and frustration. Attempts to get better hawk protection laws have often been met with indifference. And, frequently, the efforts of Dr. Broun to discourage hawk killing over the ridges around Hawk Mountain have been countered with threats of bodily harm.

The roots of prejudice against the hawks are deep. Hawk killers still sneak up to the ridges and shoot hawks. But they are no longer out in strong force. Thanks to the work of the Hawk Mountain Sanctuary, no hawk shooters congregate on Hawk Mountain or the nearby ridges. This is not because the hawk killers have had a change of heart. Rather it can be attributed to the fact that the Hawk Mountain Sanctuary has turned the spotlight of public indignation on the hawk killers. And this spotlight has proved too strong for even the most hardened hawk killer.

Hawk watching from the lookout is a thrilling experience. The top of the mountain is crowned with a mass of jumbled rocks tossed there by receding glaciers long ago. Laurel and rhododendron bushes surround the base of the rock pile. And jutting up among the rocks are stunted trees fighting the winds that whistle over the mountain.

The view from the lookout, located on the northeastern end of Hawk Mountain, is almost beyond description. To the north are the cities of the declining anthracite coal empire: Tamaqua, Hazelton, Wilkes Barre and Scranton. Over toward the northeast loom the Pocono mountains and beyond them, the Delaware River, New Jersey and New York. Southward lie the historic cities of Reading and Philadelphia. Westward is Harrisburg, the capital of Pennsylvania.

Perched high on the lookout, you have a hawk's eye view of the fertile valley below. All around, as far as you can see, are square and contoured fields. Cutting the fields into odd patterns are winding creeks, stone walls, old railroad tracks, and wind-breaks of trees and hedges. This splendid panorama is at its best in October, when the countryside is clothed in brilliant autumn foliage.

Over this colorful scenery, down the "endless mountain," come the hawks, falcons, eagles and vultures. High and low they soar, riding the strong breezes that funnel through the mountain gaps. Tacking, sailing, the hawks rush along, mile on mile, with hardly a wing beat. Even through binoculars, one fails to see any movement of the wings, except when the wind ruffles through the feathers.

What makes the hawk display over Hawk Mountain so exciting are the warm air currents or thermals rising up from the valley floor. When the wind is strong and brings many hawks over the ridges, the watchers are treated to an unusual aerial show as the hawks are buffeted aloft by the thermals.

The thermals are important to the hawks. Even though the hawks can soar for miles on the wind without flapping their wings, they gradually lose altitude. Unless they beat their wings, they will continue to descend. But when a hawk passes over a thermal, he is lifted higher and maintains his altitude.

On a good day, as many as several thousand hawks soar over Hawk Mountain. Over the lookout and to the sides, rising, falling, then lifted by a thermal, soar the red-tails, red-shoulders, broad-wings, kestrels, merlins, ospreys, harriers, and bald eagles. Occasionally, the watchers are treated to the sight of a handsome peregrine or majestic golden eagle. Or, perhaps, they may see the spectacular stoop of a falcon when he spots some prey far down in the valley.

12

Here's to the Hawks!

Follow the hawks! It can be an exciting and healthy hobby, one that will take you outdoors. No matter where you live—north, south, east or west—you'll find some species of hawk darting or soaring through the sky. And you'll have many hours of pleasure as you watch the lords of the sky.

Although you can go a-hawking without binoculars, you'll find binoculars valuable. Actually, you can see just as far with your naked eye as with the best binoculars. For example, you can see the horizon and the moon with the naked eye. But how *well* can you see them? And that is where binoculars come in handy. The hawks you see through a good pair of binoculars are enlarged, clear, and sharply defined.

Practically any kind or model of binoculars will do as a start, since a good pair is expensive. Later on, when you've saved up enough money, you can purchase a fine pair of binoculars, which should be chosen with care. High-quality binoculars are a lifetime investment and you should get those that will serve you well.

Most bird watchers prefer a 7X, 35 binocular. The first number, 7, refers to the power of magnification, the

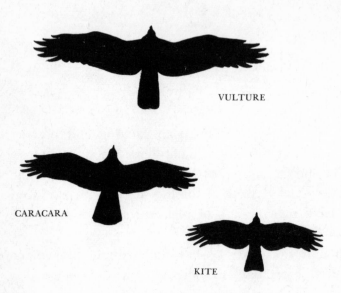

VULTURE

CARACARA

KITE

BUTEO

A bird watcher's view of the hawks,

Here's to the Hawks!

EAGLE

OSPREY

ACCIPTER

HARRIER   FALCON

eagles, kites, falcons and vultures

X is a multiplication sign and the 35 indicates the diameter, in millimeters, of the object seen through the
binoculars. Thus, a 7X, 35 binocular magnifies seven
times and the object viewed is thirty-five millimeters in
diameter.

At first, each hawk will seem like another. But gradually you will acquire skill in identifying them. In a sense,
identifying hawks is similar to identifying automobiles.
When learning to tell one automobile from another, you
concentrate on the special features of each car. It is the
same with hawks—you learn their special features or
field marks.

Learn the groups of hawks first. When you see a hawk
flying or soaring, see if you can tell in which group he be-
longs. Is he a falcon or Accipiter? Again, let us refer to
automobiles. Autos belong to groups, such as sedans,
station wagons, coupes, convertibles, etc. You usually
mentally classify a car as a sedan or station wagon, then
narrow it down to the model and year. When you spot
a hawk, you can place it in its group, then try to de-
termine the species. As for the age of the hawk, that takes
years of practice!

The chances are that most of the hawks you'll see will
be in flight. Therefore, you should know the special
features of each group as seen in the air. Here is a
handy list of the field marks of the various groups of
hawks.

Flying Field Marks of the Hawk Groups

Falcons   Long, pointed wings. They fly with rapid wing beats and stoop or dive on their prey. Look for them over open fields.

Accipiters   Short-winged hawks with long tails. They fly with several wing beats, followed by a glide or sail.

Buteos   Broad-winged hawks with square or round tails. They fly slowly, but do a great deal of soaring. Seen near and over woods.

Harrier   He sails and hovers over marshes and cut-over land. He moves up and down, quartering like a hunting dog. Look for his white rump patch.

Caracara   Long-necked hawk with white tail. Usually seen in company of vultures.

Osprey   Eagle-size, with whitish head and under-parts. He flies with a gull-like *hook* or *curve* to his wings and can hover like a kingfisher.

Eagles   Bald eagle has a white head and tail. The golden eagle is brown with golden hackles on his head. Eagles fly with powerful sweeps of their wings. They soar with wings held out flat.

Kites   Slim, swallowlike hawks with long tails. Erratic fliers, coursing here and there. They can hover and kite in one place.

Vultures   Almost always seen soaring, with wings held up from the *horizontal*—in a V or dihedral angle. They have naked heads and necks and turkeylike feet.

And so, here's to the hawks. Look for them near your home. Join the thousands of hawk watchers who flock to the hawk observation sites to see the annual fall migrations. Visit Hawk Mountain Sanctuary, if you can. Or just lie on your back on the lawn and watch a hawk lazily wheeling in the sky. Whichever you do, you'll be paying tribute to a bird that is as free as the air!

*Proud, fearless—screaming his defiance across
the wilderness*